300
Incredible
Things for Game Players
on the
Internet

300INCREDIBLE.COM, LLC
600 Village Trace, Building 23
Marietta, Georgia 30067

(800) 909-6505

ISBN 1-930435-06-1

— Dedication —

To my husband, Gary—my favorite gamer and worthy opponent.
Charlyn Chisholm

Introduction

300 Incredible Things for Game Players was written for every person who has ever stayed up all night, missed an appointment or skipped lunch hour to finish playing a game. This book will help you find new addictive games to download, learn secrets to help you have more fun with old favorites, read reviews of the latest games to buy and seek worthy opponents all over the world. Have fun, and don't forget to get some sleep!

Charlyn Chisholm
Chisholm@300INCREDIBLE.COM

Ken Leebow
Leebow@300INCREDIBLE.COM
http://www.300INCREDIBLE.com

About the Authors

Charlyn Chisholm bought her first used computer at the age of fifteen, so she could play a few games. That hobby led to a career in computers which has now spanned twelve years. Despite her many other responsibilities, she is still hooked on games.

When away from the computer, Charlyn can be found reading, gardening, solving crossword puzzles, riding roller coasters and spending time with her family.

Ken Leebow has been involved with the computer business for over twenty years. The Internet has fascinated him since he began exploring it several years ago, and he has helped over a million readers utilize its resources. Ken has appeared frequently in the media, educating individuals about the Web's greatest hits. He is considered a leading expert on what is incredible about the Internet.

When not online, you can find Ken playing tennis, running, reading or spending time with his family. He is living proof that being addicted to the Net doesn't mean giving up on the other pleasures of life.

Acknowledgments

Putting a book together requires many expressions of appreciation. The following people deserve special thanks:

- Charlyn's husband—Gary—who never complained about the amount of time she spent glued to the computer.

- Charlyn's parents—who always encouraged her to attempt any challenge that came her way.

- Ken's family—Denice, Alissa and Josh—for being especially supportive during the writing of the book.

- Paul Joffe and Janet Bolton, of *TBI Creative Services*, for their editing and graphics skills.

- Mark Krasner and Janice Caselli for sharing the vision of the book and helping make it a reality.

The Incredible Internet Book Series

TABLE OF CONTENTS

		Page	Sites

TABLE OF CONTENTS (continued)

CHAPTER 1
FREE FUN

1
In the Know

http://www.gamedemo.com
Keep informed about the latest games and demos, and download DOS and Windows versions in categories from "Action" to "Sports." Reviews by fellow gamers will help you avoid wasting time on the duds.

2
Only the Best

http://www.happypuppy.com/top10
Legendary game site Happy Puppy points you to the top ten downloadable game demos. Find out for yourself why these are so popular.

3
Adrenaline Rush

http://www.adrenalinevault.com/pcrl
By putting them right on the front, this site makes it easy to see the latest demos. If you're having technical trouble with a game, download a patch to fix it.

4
C|Net

http://www.gamecenter.com/Downloads

http://shareware.cnet.com

Search C|Net's database for shareware and freeware, or scroll down for the "Games" category. The Gamecenter has demos to download and try.

5
Live the Game

http://www.gamesdomain.com/directd

The Games Domain gives you demos, downloads of shareware and freeware games and game patches for Windows and DOS. Can't get enough? Download a theme for your favorite game to decorate your desktop.

6
Get in the Zone

http://zone.msn.com/download.asp

The Microsoft Network's Gaming Zone points you to the top five downloads for the PC, in every category from "Action" to "Strategy."

7
A Game a Day

http://www.demoland.com
http://www.dailydemo.com
These sites give you your daily dose of games to download. They list the most popular downloads, too, so you can follow the crowd.

8
Hot Files

http://www.hotfiles.com/games.html
ZDNet's database includes games for the PC, Mac and even the Palm Pilot. Now you can take your games anywhere.

9
The Best Things In Life

http://www.freegamesweb.com
http://www.gameshead.com
Who says you can't get something for nothing? These sites have great games to download. And they're all free!

10
Free For All

http://www.free-games-net.com
Download shareware and freeware games for fans of action, racing, RPG (Role Playing Games) and puzzles.

11
Old and New

http://www.gameplayer.com
http://www.gameplayer.com/unwanted
This site claims to update every fifteen minutes, so you can get your hands on the very latest downloads. The Unwanted Game Room stores old IBM and Commodore 64 games.

12
Demo It Free

http://www.gamex.net/downloads
http://www.demoplanet.com
Try before you buy with these free demos. No matter what types of games you prefer—action, RPG, sports, strategy games, flight simulators or arcade—you'll find it at these sites. Just choose your game and go!

13
Puzzler's Paradise

http://www.programfiles.com
You can choose from 1,600 games in many different categories, from Bingo to Trivia to Tetris-type puzzle games. If you need more action, there are arcade games, too.

14
Turbo Drive

http://www.3dfiles.com
This site allows you to download freeware, shareware and screensavers that take advantage of 3D accelerator cards for the PC.

15
Fit to Print

http://www.cdmag.com
Computer Games Magazine's site brings you new demo games each month. Past games are listed in a long A–Z list. You can't get that at the newsstand!

16
Hot Games

http://pc.hotgames.com
http://www.gamepage.nl/download
Download (fast) the hottest games for the PC, listed alphabetically or by genre.

17
An Arcade in Your PC

http://www.download.net/arcade
http://www.download.net/msgboard
Miss those old arcade games from the 80s? Save your quarters and download them here. Check the messageboard for the word on the best (and worst) downloads.

18
Windows NT

http://ntware.ntware.com/games
Running on NT? Don't feel left out. Download games meant just for you.

19
Back to Basics
http://users.deltanet.com/users/phixus/kgames
Here are new versions of old DOS arcade classics, from the man who brought you Mario Teaches Typing and SimCity.

20
Jukebox Jam
http://gemsgames.game-point.net
This site has a Jukebox you can set in a separate window that will play music while you play games. Maybe the Mission Impossible theme song will get you in the mood to win.

CHAPTER II
WHAT'S NEW?

21
Game Spot

http://www.gamespot.com
ZDNet's site covers all games, or you can customize it to show just the types of games you like. You'll also find cheats, game guides and downloads at this mega-site.

22
Daily Radar

http://www.dailyradar.com
Daily Radar combines up-to-the-minute gaming and entertainment news. Check here for walkthroughs of games on all platforms, with plenty of pictures to help you through the tough spots.

23
Happy Puppy

http://www.happypuppy.com
One of the oldest and most popular gaming sites, Happy Puppy reviews games for the PC, Dreamcast, PlayStation and Nintendo 64. You'll also find downloads and links to fun Web games.

24
That's Entertainment

http://www.ign.com
IGN covers the entertaining side of games, with news and interviews with the people behind games and movies.

25
Games First

http://www.gamesfirst.com
Here are well-written and helpful reviews of all the latest games, plus some tips on installing and playing your favorites.

26
Computing Central
http://computingcentral.msn.com/topics/computergames
Microsoft's site features PC game reviews, messageboards and chats. Talk to other gamers, and hear from the game creators themselves.

27
The Name Says It All
http://www.videogames.com
If you can't get the picture from reading all the news, reviews and previews at this site from ZDNet, just download a video trailer for that new game, and you'll see all the action before it's even released.

28
New Game Time
http://www.consoledomain.com
Don't wait for the next console game to hit the shelves. Get a sneak peek at all the upcoming action for PlayStation 2, Dreamcast, Nintendo 64 and Gameboy.

300 Incredible Things for Game Players on the Internet • II: What's New?

11

29
Adventure Awaits

http://www.adventurecollective.com
http://www.adventuregamer.com
http://www.justadventure.com
Ready to explore? Get rumors, previews and demos of the latest adventure games.

30
Game Informer

http://www.gameinformer.com
http://www.gamefan.com
Here are no-holds-barred reviews of the latest games for Nintendo 64, PlayStation and Dreamscape. If you can't wait, these sites are where you should go to find a lot of screen shots.

31
Don't Miss a Thing

http://www.gamex.net
Gamex posts daily bug reports which help you avoid hours of frustration. You'll also find up-to-the-minute news of the gaming world, reviews of new titles and the latest demos to download.

32
3D Action

http://www.3dactionplanet.com

For gamers who are serious about action games, this site has news, game reviews and feature articles on such subjects as upgrading your gaming machine.

33
Nintendo

http://www.nintendo.com

Nintendo's official site has news and previews of upcoming games for Super NES, Nintendo 64 and Game Boy.

34
Nintendo Extras

http://www.tendoproject.com
http://www.nintendojo.com
http://www.nintendorks.com

If Nintendo is your game, bookmark these sites. You'll be the first to know what's happening on Mario's favorite system.

35
Nintendo Talk

http://www.tendobox.com
Find fellow Nintendo fans and swap stories, tips, opinions and secrets.

36
Code Name: Dolphin

http://www.planetn2000.com
This site provides some speculation, rumors and even a bit of news about Nintendo's next-generation system.

37
Sony Playstation

http://www.playstation.com
Sony's official site has news, game info and an online store. Visit the Underground for secrets straight from the source.

38
Playstation Extras
http://www.sonysource.com/shtml/main.shtml
http://www.vidgames.com
These guys are serious about the Playstation. Check out this 24/7 newsroom for around-the-clock news on Sony's gaming platform, and you won't ever miss a thing.

39
PlayStation 2
http://www.ps2k.net
Here's the latest on the next-generation console system from Sony.

40
PlayStation 2 Extras
http://www.psxnation.com
http://www.playstationfan.com
Get more news, previews and secrets from the biggest fans of Sony's games.

41
Sega Dreamscape
http://www.sega.com
Sega's site lets you order the Dreamcast system, read about upcoming releases and get game secrets. Plus, take a peek behind the scenes at how some of the games are created.

42
Dreamscape Talk
http://communities.msn.com/SegaCentral/homepage
Connect with some of the other fans of Sega's Dreamscape games, and learn their winning secrets.

43
Dreamscape Extras
http://www.segadreamcast.net
http://www.seganet.com
http://www.dreamcast.net
Get the "unofficial" scoop on games for the Dreamcast.

"I PROMISE WE'LL PLAY SOME MORE COMPUTER GAMES AFTER SCHOOL. NOW GO BACK HOME! GO!!!"

44
Game Boy
http://www.gameboy.com
Nintendo's handheld video game has an official site with games, previews and news about the next-generation system (code name: Advance).

45
Game Boy Extras
http://www.the-gadgeteer.com/gameboy.html
http://www.absolutegb.com
Link up with other Game Boy fans, find game reviews and learn some game secrets and strategies.

46
The Gaming Place
http://gamingplace.siol.net/games.htm
Here are reviews of all kinds of games, including action and adventure, puzzles, sports and more.

18

300 Incredible Things for Game Players on the Internet • II: What's New?

47
Hot Games

http://www.hotgames.com
Serious gamers can preview the latest PC and console games here. Games are reviewed by editors, but you can add your own two cents by rating the game or posting a review.

48
Review Planet

http://reviewplanet.com
Why take one game reviewer's word for it? This site lets anyone who has played the game submit an opinion. After you've read what everyone else thinks, submit your own review.

49
Computer Gaming Online

http://www.cdmag.com
You may have to dig a little for information at this cluttered site, but it's worth it. You'll find reviews of the hottest games, gaming news, hints and tips.

50
Speak Up

http://www.videogamereview.com
http://www.pcgamereview.com
Who needs the critics? Write your own reviews of the best and worst games. You can also read what other gamers have to say.

51
Extreme Action

http://www.actionxtreme.com
Extreme gamers, check in at this site. It covers the whole world of action, RPG, strategy and sim games.

52
Buyer Beware

http://www.productopia.com
http://www.us.buy.com/retail/toc.asp?loc=363
PlayStation, Dreamcast and Nintendo are some of the major game systems. If you need help, check these buyer's guides before you purchase.

20

300 Incredible Things for Game Players on the Internet • II: What's New?

53
Interactive Fiction

http://interactfiction.about.com
http://www.xyzzynews.com
http://www.textfire.com

It's an "ancient" (in Web terms) art form that is still alive and well. Unlike modern video games, which tend to look like movies or cartoons, an Interactive Fiction game reads like a good novel. These sites will point you to the best of these games.

54
Bingo

http://www.bingobugle.com

If your days are filled with thoughts of Bingo, this site is for you. Check your lucky days before heading out to the Bingo parlor, talk to other Bingoers or join the Bingo Cruise (a worldwide championship tournament).

55
GameDad

http://www.gamedad.com

GameDad gives you the skinny on the games your kids want. He describes them and rates them high to low on violence, blood and gore, nudity and moral issues.

300 Incredible Things for Game Players on the Internet • II: What's New?

21

56
Link Goldmine

http://gamerplanet.com

This site looks like the Yahoo! of gaming sites. You'll find links to news, reviews and previews for every platform from the PC to PlayStation.

57
Ant People

http://www.ant.com

This game site, which was launched on America Online a few years ago, has taken to the Web. You'll find reviews of the best and worst games on all platforms, daily polls, rants and raves and a chance to join the Ant Army.

58
Sports Gamer

http://www.interlog.com/~gardiner/sgamer1.htm

This is the online version of Sports Gamer magazine. You can find a list of online sports leagues and links to sports game sites of all kinds.

59
Game Report

http://www.gamereport.com
This online version of The Game Report is dedicated to news and reviews of board, dice, card, family and strategy games.

CHAPTER III
BEAT THE SYSTEM

60
Tip Sheet

http://www.gamecenter.com/Tipcheat

You'll find tips to help you beat the newest PC and console games, plus links to online strategy guides.

61
Cheat to Win

http://cheats.gamez.com

Need a leg up on the competition? This site claims to be the largest game cheat search engine on the Internet. Over 90,000 cheats are listed, covering games for the PC, Macintosh and all the home video game (console) systems.

62
Walk Me Through It

http://guides.ign.com

If you're stuck in a game, this site can give you a little push in the right direction. You'll find complete walkthroughs of games on all platforms. A walkthrough is all the information you'll need to get to the end of the game with your sanity intact.

63
Just the FAQs

http://www.gamefaqs.com

If you have questions about a game, this is the place to go. You'll find a massive database of FAQs (Frequently Asked Questions) for games on most platforms, including PC games, console platforms (including Nintendo 64 and Sega Dreamcast) and even arcade games.

64
Ask For Help

http://www.gamerzone.com

If the cheats section doesn't answer your question, use the TipSwap to consult with other gamers.

65
Cheat Crazy

http://www.cheatplanet.com
http://www.cheatcc.com
http://www.cheatland.com
http://www.cheaterskrypt.com
http://www.worlddesign.net
http://www.cheatindex.com
http://www.hotcheats.com

You'll get a leg up on the competition with all the cheat codes and strategy secrets at these sites. They cover PC games as well as console games like Nintendo 64.

66
Tell Me How To Cheat

http://www.xcheater.com

Look in the "Cheat Tools" section to download what you'll need to get that ultra-high score. The "Cheat Help" section will tell you how to use them.

67
Word to the Wise

http://sages.ign.com
You can browse cheat codes (almost 50,000 of them) for the latest games on Dreamcast, PC, PlayStation and Nintendo 64, or search the cheat codes for that game you're stuck on. The site also has FAQs and previews of upcoming games.

68
Just Give Me A Hint

http://www.uhs-hints.com
http://www.cheatgoat.com
If you're stuck on a game but don't want to ruin the ending, try the Universal Hint System. They give you only the hints you need to get through that tough puzzle.

69
Cheat Club

http://www.cheaters-guild.com
http://www.cheat-elite.com
http://www.freaky-cheats.com
Find cheat codes and walkthroughs of thousands of games, listed alphabetically. Check out the surprises in the Easter Eggs section.

70
Game Shark

http://www.gameshark.com
A Gameshark is an accessory you can buy for your home console system. Plug it in, log in the right codes and presto — extra lives, rapid fire and infinite health.

71
Take It To The Next Level

http://www.n64-cheats.com
http://www.psxtreme.com
http://www.ps2cool.com
http://www.gbfrenzy.com
http://www.dcmania.com
Here are more hints, cheats, FAQs and walkthroughs for various platforms.

72
Spell It Out For Me

http://kraven.simplenet.com
Besides cheat codes, you'll find level codes, maps, moves, saved games and anything else you need to cheat your way through the latest games.

73
Don't Blow It

http://www.game-critic.com
Make sure a game is worth your money before you buy it. At this site, you'll find reviews of games for the PC, PlayStation and Dreamcast.

74
Ask, and You Shall Receive

http://www.gamestats.com/tips
If you can't find the cheats for a game, e-mail the folks at Gamestats and ask. They'll send it to you.

75
Nintendo Cheats

http://www.n64gamer.com
http://www.n64cc.com
These sites will give you the cheat codes for the top ten Nintendo games. There's also a special section on endings, so you can find out what happens when the game is won (even when you can't quite get there yourself).

CHAPTER IV
IT'S A DUEL

76
Climb Aboard

http://www.station.sony.com
The Sony Station is the online home of such classics as Jeopardy, Wheel of Fortune and Trivial Pursuit. Play against others across the Internet; it's more fun than TV.

77
Deal Me In

http://hoyle.won.net
All the Hoyle card game classics are here — cribbage, spades, hearts, bridge, gin and more. They'll hook you up with opponents and partners.

78
Yahoo! Games

http://games.yahoo.com
Go to Yahoo! Games to play classic games like backgammon and chess; card games like blackjack, bridge and poker; and fantasy sports like auto racing and baseball. There's always someone ready for a game.

79
Age of Empires

http://www.zone.com/aoe
http://www.zone.com/age2
http://www.zone.com/aoeror

Age of Empires is a real-time strategy adventure game that spans an epic 10,000 years. You get to play the leader of a stone age tribe. Develop your tribe into world explorers, conquerors or the richest civilization known to man. Play alone or against other tribes.

80
Alien vs. Predator

http://www.mplayer.com/gamers/action/avp

Pick your species — Colonial Marine, Predator or Alien — and fight to save it in this nightmarish, futuristic environment.

81
Quake

http://www.won.net/channels/action/quake2
http://www.zone.com/quake2
http://www.mplayer.com/gamers/action
http://www.kali.net/js/games/quake2
One of the most popular multi-player games of all time, Quake has two sequels and a number of variations. Jump into the action from any site and start shooting!

82
Kali

http://www.kali.net
Kali is the world's largest Internet gaming network. Join more than 250,000 players in 40 countries who compete in popular games like Duke Nukem and Age of Empires.

83
Kahn

http://kahn.descent4.org
Kahn offers free software that lets you play such popular games as Descent and Quake against other players.

84
Mplayer

http://www.mplayer.com
Crush your friends—or complete strangers—over the Internet. Mplayer has over 80 games to choose from, including action, strategy, board games and card games. While you play, use Voice Chat to talk trash to your friends.

85
Link Up and Play

http://www.playlink.com
This site's games are a little offbeat. Play Gario Brothers, and see if you can survive as a child star. Or, play a classic in a new way—Blocktionary lets you build bigger and better words and rack up points against your opponents.

86
The Zone

http://www.zone.com
The Microsoft Gaming Zone has thousands of people playing dozens of games. Jump in any time, and join the competition. Games are free and include such card games as spades, retail games such as Rogue Spear and premium games like Asheron's Call.

87
Meet Your Match

http://www.westwood.com/choice.html

This site will hook you up with opponents to play Tiberian Sun, Red Alert 2, Command and Conquer and other games of skill.

88
Up Until 2 AM?

http://www.2amgames.com

Some of these games can keep you up all night. Download 2 AM Games' software and play against others in such games as Chain of Command, Alliance and Defiance and Total War.

89
Quake

http://www.idsoftware.com

Ready for a deathmatch? Download Quake and Quake II software and play the registered versions of the games with other players over a modem.

90
Star Craft

http://www.blizzard.com/starcraft
http://www.starcraft.org
This game puts the fate of the galaxy in your hands. Recruit and train your forces, then lead them to victory (or crushing defeat) in an intergalactic battle. There are thirty unique missions to challenge you.

91
Turn Up the Heat

http://www.heat.net
Heat is a network that lets you join popular multiplayer games like 10Six, Quake, Kingpin, Age of Empires and Baldurs Gate.

92
Talk It Out

http://www.oceanline.com
Oceanline's Chat 'n' Play lets you chat and play with other gamers. Games include sports, simulations and classic arcade games.

93
Sports Action

http://gametropolis.com

Download the free Gametropolis software to play arcade and sports action games against others. Games include BFL Football and Mission: Moon.

94
Classic Fun

http://www.won.net

Turn off your brain and have some fun. You can play card, board, casino games (even craps), strategy, action, game shows and puzzle games. There's always someone to play against. Enjoy!

95
Adventure Awaits

http://www.igame.net

Jump into a role-playing, adventure or MUD (Multi-User Dungeon) game, already in progress. What are you waiting for?

96
The World Is in Your Hands

http://www.worldgame.org/networldgame
Have aspirations of world domination? Try the NetWorld Game, an Internet-based simulation of the world.

97
Go Underground

http://www.godlike.com/muds/muds.html
http://www.mudconnect.com
http://www.apocalypse.org/pub/u/lpb/muddex
These sites connect you to MUDs (Multi-User Dungeons) and MUSHes (Multi-User Shared Hallucination) throughout the Web. If you're new to any of the games, check out the tutorials.

98
Explore Different Worlds

http://anguish.org
http://www.aurora.org.au
http://www.angband.com/towers
http://www.valheru.com

Pick one of these MUDs for an adventure set in ancient times, in a modern-day town, in the Lord of the Rings stories or in a dungeons-and-dragons setting.

99
Chase The Cheese

http://www.tim.org

Create your own character in the world's oldest running MUSH and collect more cheese than anyone else.

100
The World's a Stage

http://www.roleplayinggames.net

This is the site of a free club devoted to playing Role Playing Games online. You can join in with others playing RPGs on the message boards. Games include Star Wars and Advanced Dungeons & Dragons.

101
Star Trekking

http://www.jps.net/mattu
This Web Ring can connect you with Star Trek Role-Playing Games of all types across the galaxy. Join the fleet!

102
Doomed

http://www.doomshack.com
http://www.kali.net/js/games/doom
http://www.gamers.org/dhs
In this, the original 3-D shoot-em-up, walk through the halls and kill whatever you find. These sites let you log on and play against others on the Net. They won't know what hit them!

CHAPTER V
GO FOR THE GOLD

103
Take Five

http://www.boxerjam.com
Pick the game you're best at—puzzles, word games or trivia—and compete with other players for prizes.

104
Big Bucks

http://www.uproar.com/contest
This site is the home of Big Bucks Blowout Bingo and the CNN Trivia Blitz. Cash prizes range from $5 all the way to $5,000.

105
Virtual Vegas

http://www.virtualvegas.com
Play such classic casino games as slots and roulette for free, as long as you want. You'll win tokens you can then trade for prizes, and unlike a real casino, it won't cost you a dime.

106
Variety is the Spice of Life

http://www.pogo.com
http://www.iwin.com

These sites have something for you, no matter what you like to play. You can join in with other players in card and board games, prediction games, word games, trivia, puzzle games like Animal Ark and casino games like roulette and Bingo. Many of the games reward you with cash and prizes.

107
It's Raining Tokens

http://www.prizecentral.com
http://www.won.net

These two sites merged, so there are now twice as many games to play. Win tokens to trade for prizes, from a Disney World vacation to a big screen TV. The games range from classics like Space Invaders and Tetris, to prediction games such as Market Psychic and Pick the Oscars.

"IT'S NOT A NICOTINE PATCH, IT'S A NINTENDO CARTRIDGE. I'M ADDICTED!"

108
Hit the Jackpot

http://www.jackpot.com
http://www.freeslot.com
Spin the reels of a virtual slot machine for a chance to win up to $1,000,000.

109
Get Your Share

http://www.gamesville.com
Gamesville gives out over $100,000 in prize money every month. Play slot machines, Bingo or card games like Acey-Deucy for a piece of the pie.

110
Win the Lottery

http://www.pluslotto.com
http://www.iwin.com/xtreme/lotto
http://www.thebirthdaygame.com
Play the lottery every day, but keep those dollars in your pocket. These free lotteries give you the chance to win up to five million dollars.

111
Riddle Me This

http://www.riddler.com
Play trivia, crossword puzzles and word games against others. You can win t-shirts and watches. Some of the winners are randomly selected, so you don't have to be a champion to win a prize.

112
Stock Up

http://game.etrade.com
http://maxinvest.lycos.com
http://contest.finance.yahoo.com/t1?u
Trade stocks with a hundred grand of someone else's money. If you win the game, you win real money.

113
I've got BINGO

http://www.bingo.com
http://bingo1.women.net
It's like having a Bingo parlor on your screen. Play against others and compete for cash and gift certificates to your favorite stores.

114
Go Pro

http://us.battletop.com

Can you really make a living playing video games? Go for it with the American Internet Gaming League.

115
Scratch Off

http://www.prizes.com

If you like to play those instant-win scratch-off cards, you'll love this site. Play for cash and tokens.

116
Speedy Prizes

http://www.speedyclick.com

Earn SpeedyBucks by playing Keno, Inquizzition and Frog Hunt. Trade your SpeedyBucks for logo merchandise (such as hats and shirts) or use them to buy unusual items in the Barter Auction.

117
Addicted to Games

http://www.addictionzone.com
Play classic games and trivia for jewelry, trips and cash. You'll even be rewarded for recommending friends to the site by receiving a duplicate of whatever prize they win.

118
Sweet Surprises

http://www.candystand.com
http://www.nabiscoworld.com
Play Shockwave games with candy and junk food themes. The prizes are sweet, too — electronics and video games.

119
Prize Links

http://www.huronline.com
There are a lot of ways to win on this site. You'll find links to contests, sweepstakes and Bingo games for cash and prizes. Good luck!

120
Be A Contender

http://www.beacontender.com
Manage a virtual hockey team and compete for cash.

CHAPTER VI
JUST FOR GRINS

121
Go Bezerk

http://www.bezerk.com
This site is home to two of the most popular games on the Internet. You Don't Know Jack is a fast paced trivia gameshow with a wisecracking host. Acrophobia is a word game that will have you in stitches.

122
Shockwave

http://www.shockwave.com
The Shockwave official site has more than a hundred action, arcade, puzzle and sports games.

123
Shocking Fun

http://www.segasoft.com/lab
Segasoft's Shockwave Laboratory has concocted online games for your enjoyment. You'll find Bible Bonk, the Scud-Shooting Gallery and Zombie Dinner, to name a few.

124
More Shocking

http://shockwavegames.hypermart.net
http://games.looksmart.com
http://www.happypuppy.com/web
These sites link to even more Shockwave games across the Web.

125
On the Scene

http://www.gamescene.com
Uproar's Gamescene is home to such unique Shockwave puzzle games as Event Horizon, strategy games like Smite Thee! and action games such as AstroBall.

126
Amusing Antics

http://www.amused.com
This site, the Centre for the Easily Amused, has enough diversions to keep you playing (and laughing) for days.

127
Java Blitz

http://www.shockblitz.com
Play a variety of Java games in categories of arcade, action, sports and puzzles.

128
Mr. Showbiz

http://mrshowbiz.go.com/games
http://mrshowbiz.go.com/games/surgery/friends
Mr. Showbiz has celebrity games galore. Play Headless Horseman Hangman or Star Wars Trivia. Feeling creative? Head over to the Friends plastic surgery lab, where you can mix and match features of Ross, Rachel and Phoebe.

129
South Park Pinball

http://www.comedycentral.com/southpark/pinball
Cartman, Stan, Kyle and Kenny have their own pinball game, and it's here on the Web. Save your quarters and play online.

130
Web Crawler

http://www.stanlee.net/games
Comic book legend Stan Lee has some cool, high-tech games on his site. Blow away bad guys in Bubble Madness, or go dimension-hopping in The 7th Portal.

131
Clevermedia

http://clevermedia.com/arcade
At Clevermedia, you can play dozens of games, from educational to arcade.

132
Game Land

http://www.game-land.com
Whether you prefer to use your brains or your reflexes, there are plenty of games here to test your skill. Play card, arcade and logic games.

133
Fun Planet

http://usa.funplanet.com
Fun Planet adds different games to its site all the time. Play for fun or small prizes. The games are simple but unusual, and they also offer classic games like blackjack and Bug Invaders.

134
Just Have Fun

http://www.pimpernel.com/games.html
http://www.gamegate.com/games
Play all the classics—Mah Jongg, crossword puzzles, concentration, board games, super Tetris, blackjack and slot machines. They're online, and they're all free.

135
Java Arcade

http://www.javaarcade.com
Try out lots of Java games of all types, including classic interactive fiction from legendary game creator Scott Adams.

136
Space Pirate

http://www.spacepirate.com
Explore and plunder the galaxy while amassing a crew, fame and fortune.

137
Game Central

http://www.gamecenter.com/Play
C|Net's Gamecenter has links to online gaming sites in every category, from game shows to fantasy sports.

138
Arcade Online

http://www.arcadegamesonline.com
You'll find Java and Shockwave games of all kinds at this site — arcade, casino, classic board games, card games and movie and sports games.

139
Board Games

http://www.darkfish.com
Play online versions of such favorite board games as Checkers and Reversi, or try a new one like Nim Skulls.

140
Game Break

http://www.garrink.com/garrben/demo.html
http://www.freestuffcenter.com/sub/multishocktop.html
http://www.quadgames.com
Need something different? These sites offer a variety of unique, free Shockwave games like Time Travel Pod, Little Piggy Races and Herman's Pond.

141
Mootown

http://www.mootown.com
For you bovine lovers, there are six games in Mootown, including Moo Tunes and Highway Madness.

142
Fun Zone

http://www.afunzone.com
This huge site has over 750 pages of games and puzzles, such as Alpine Ski and Klondike.

143
Photo Hunt

http://www.photohunt.com
Grab a camera and go on a virtual photo shoot in the wilderness. Explore to capture the best shots, then compete with other photographers for the prize.

144
Dunk the Media

http://www.four-corners.com/media.htm
All those negative news shows got you down? Show the media folks how you feel with a good round of Media Dunk Tank. Feel better now?

145
Toy Box

http://toybox.asap.net/shockmon
ShockMonkey brings you such odd but fun games as Whack-A-Mole, Space Truckin'
and Virtual Heckler.

146
Find More Games

http://games.looksmart.com
http://www.looksmart.com/sitewatch/games
http://www.excite.com/games
Bored? Got a few hours to waste? These sites point to a variety of free games on
the Internet. You'll find plenty of ways to pass a pleasant afternoon.

CHAPTER VII
THRILLS AND CHILLS

147
Microsoft Arcade

http://zone.msn.com/hub_arcade.asp

http://zone.msn.com/hub_action.asp

Microsoft's online arcade has a few video games such as Frogger, and a lot of action games like Rogue Spear and Quake II.

148
Tune Up Your Game

http://www.microsoft.com/games

The Microsoft folks' gaming site has patches, demos and extras for their adventure and action games.

149
Turbo Charge Your PC

http://www.wickedpc.com

Today's fast-paced, graphics-intensive games take some major hardware to run. This site for serious gamers covers equipment you can buy to supercharge your system.

150
Remember When They Cost a Quarter?

http://www.hasbrointeractive.com/atari/online_games

Hasbro's site gives a home on the Web to classic Atari games. You can play Shockwave versions of classic 80s arcade games like Centipede, Frogger, Missile Command and Super Breakout.

151
It's All About the Games

http://videogames.about.com

http://compactiongames.about.com

About.com's guides to video games and console games provide great resources for gamers. You'll find news, reviews and links to games all over the Web.

152
A Classic Arcade on Your PC

http://www.mame.net

Can't find a classic arcade near you? Play those fabulous 80s games on your own PC. First, you'll need a program like MAME (Multiple Arcade Machine Emulator) to bring old favorites like Defender back to life.

153
Just Like Old Times

http://www.emunews.net

http://members.aol.com/deliriumth/emarcade.htm

Look for links to emulators for classic arcade games, console games like Nintendo and computer systems including the old Apple II.

154
Choose Your Game

http://www.arcadeathome.com
http://www.classicgaming.com
http://www.houseofarcadia.com
http://www.vintagegaming.com

Once you get an emulator, you'll need game ROMs for each game you want to play. These sites have ROMs for games such as Ms. Pac Man and Asteroids.

155
Don't Leave Mac Out

http://www.macmame.org

Here are classic arcade game emulators for Macintosh computers.

156
Reads Like a Novel, Plays Like a Game

http://interactfiction.about.com

Tired of games that are all flash and no brains? Looking for a good storyline? Try Interactive Fiction. Many of the classic games are here, playable on the Web (thanks to Java). If you're just getting started, this site has an excellent introduction to this type of game.

157
Interactive Fiction

http://www.tangrams.com/IF

This site links to award-winning Interactive Fiction games, and there are dozens available. Be a crime-fighting pizza delivery boy in Reverberations, or a teddy bear in A Bear's Night Out.

158
Don't Panic!

http://www.douglasadams.com/creations/infocomjava.html

Douglas Adams' classic "The Hitchhiker's Guide to the Galaxy" lives online for you to play (or replay) as an Interactive Fiction game. This is a must-see for fans of Adams' funny science fiction novels.

159
Relive the Magic

http://www.classicgaming.com/locations

Longing for a good, old-fashioned game of Pac Man? Classic Gaming maintains a list of real-life arcades, listed by state, where you can play classic video games.

160
Java Break

http://www.macrosquishy.com

This site points you to some of the best free Java games on the Web. They'll even help you write your own game.

161
Try Before You Buy

http://www.gamescapestudios.com

Download free trial versions of very cool 3D arcade games, like Mars Mission and Asteroid Impact.

162
In The Beginning

http://www.pong-story.com

It all had to start somewhere. Read the story of the first video game ever written. Pong, video gamers everywhere salute you!

163
Open An Arcade In Your House

http://www.gamearchive.com
http://www.coinoptech.com
Tired of putting your quarters into other people's game machines? Here's everything you ever needed to know about buying, selling and fixing classic video games and pinball machines.

164
Remakeover

http://www.thelogbook.com/phosphor
Sometimes a remake is even better than the original. This site reviews classic games that have been rewritten for today's gaming systems.

CHAPTER VIII
ON THE (VIRTUAL) TABLE

165
Play a Classic Game

http://www.playsite.com
Looking for someone to play Backgammon against? Can't find enough people for a game of Bridge? This site always has someone willing to play. You can choose classic board games like chess, or card games such as Hearts.

166
Trivial Pursuit

http://www.station.sony.com/trivialpursuit/genus
Broaden your trivia knowledge by playing online Trivial Pursuit for fun, prizes and bragging rights.

167
Backgammon

http://www.bkgm.com
http://www.fibs.com
http://www.cyberarts.com
http://www.vog.ru/backgammon
http://www.gammon.com

There's something for every skill level, from beginner to expert. Read the official rules, improve your game, find online opponents and hone your skills against the computer.

168
You vs. the Computer

http://www.bkgm.com/motif.html
http://freepages.pavilion.net/users/iansc

Practice your backgammon strategies with these Java games, where they pit you against a computer opponent. You'll become so good, your friends won't know what hit them!

"I've been playing Monopoly on the internet...
but I didn't know I was using my online bank account!"

169
Chess

http://www.ichess.com
http://www.chessclub.com
http://www.kasparovchess.com
Challenge yourself and improve your skills by joining an online chess game.

170
Become a Chess Master

http://www.uschess.org
http://members.aol.com/manusfealy
Feed your fascination for this complex game. Find lessons, strategies and leagues for every level, from beginner to expert.

171
Monopoly

http://www.monopoly.com
This official site of capitalism's favorite game gives you background information, tips and tricks and news from the monopoly world. You can even vote for the best token.

172
Scrabble

http://www.scrabble.com

http://www.teleport.com/~stevena/scrabble

What do you do with that Q? These sites have the answer, along with expert tips. While you're playing the game, sneak away to the computer and use the anagram builder. Just type in your letters, and you'll get some words.

173
Go To Battle

http://www.bluedogmultimedia.com/battleintro.htm

Set your ships, launch your missiles and dodge your opponent. This site has a Shockwave version of Battleship you can play online.

174
Show Your Skill

http://www.gamecolony.com

Play chess, checkers and Gin Rummy against other players, over the Net.

175
Mad Blibs

http://www.blibs.com

If you're a fan of MadLibs, try Blibs. Fill out the form with your own nouns, verbs and adjectives; then press the button and enjoy the results.

176
Solitaire

http://www.solitairegames.com

Get hooked on these addictive games. You'll find all your favorite solitaire games, plus a few you've probably never played before.

177
Magic: The Gathering

http://www.wizards.com/Magic/Welcome.asp

This is the trading card game's official site. New players can learn how to get started. Experienced players can find leagues, chat with other players and even become certified judges.

178
Learn How to Play

http://www.pagat.com
This amazing site lists rules and instructions for card games of all types from around the world. Card games are listed alphabetically as well as by type (such as Fishing Games or Trick-Taking Games).

179
Mah Jongg

http://www.mahjongg.com
http://beachsite.com/majexchange
Learn to play this ancient game of tiles. The exchange lets you trade tiles with other players around the world.

180
Go

http://gtl.jeudego.org
http://www.well.com/user/mmcadams/gointro.html
Learn to master the ultimate game of strategy. If you've never played before, brush up on the rules here. Then, battle the computer and watch your game improve.

CHAPTER IX
COME ON DOWN

181
Go Bezerk

http://www.bezerk.com

Bezerk's popular site is the home of the Net show You Don't Know Jack, as well as Acrophobia, Cosmic Consensus and Get the Picture.

182
Take Five

http://www.boxerjam.com/gameshows

This site, founded by Jeopardy co-creator Julann Griffin, is the home of such popular Internet game shows as Take 5 Entertainment and Take 5 Sports. You can compete against online opponents for prizes.

183
Want To Be A Millionaire?

http://abc.go.com/primetime/millionaire
http://www.mindfun.com/millionaire
ABC's prime time show has an online version of the game. There's no Regis, and you can't win any real money. But you can practice for your big break on the show.

184
Spin The Wheel

http://www.station.sony.com/wheel
http://www.spe.sony.com/tv/shows/wheel
Play Sony's online version of Wheel of Fortune against other players. Check out the Wheel's official site for a behind-the-scenes look at the popular game show.

185
Jeopardy

http://www.station.sony.com/jeopardy
http://www.station.sony.com/collegejeopardy
If you can win these online Jeopardy games against opponents from all over the Net, you can be as smug as Alex. Choose your game — there are versions for single-player, multi-player, sports and college.

186
Win Ben Stein's Money
http://www.comcentral.com/bstein
Comedy Central's silly but tough trivia game show has gone online. Play against computer contestants and then against the cyber version of Ben Stein for his cyber money. (Yes, that means you won't win real money.)

187
Hit the Big Time
http://marketing.cbs.com/network/tvshows/daytime/shows/price/tickets.shtml
http://www.spe.sony.com/tv/shows/wheel
Get on television and (maybe) win some prizes. The Price Is Right and Wheel of Fortune are always looking for a few good players. Too shy to be a contestant? You can pick up some free tickets and watch from the studio audience.

188
Win Millions
http://www.fox.com/specials/greed/registration.html
http://www.nbc.com/twentyone/contact.html
http://abc.go.com/primetime/millionaire
http://entertainment.cbs.com/network/tvshows/primetime/shows/winninglines
For the really big prizes, go to these sites to find out how you can compete for a million dollars on national television.

189
In Real Jeopardy
http://www.spe.sony.com/tv/shows/jeopardy
http://www.spe.sony.com/tv/shows/rockjeopardy/csearch.html
Do you have what it takes to compete in the big leagues? Find out when and where the next contestant searches are for Jeopardy and Rock and Roll Jeopardy. There will be a quiz!

190
Find Love Online

http://www.spe.sony.com/tv/shows/dating/contestant.html
http://www.changeofheart.com/cmp/signup2.htm
Playing The Dating Game, or Having a Change of Heart? These sites will tell you how to compete on the actual television game shows of those names.

191
Laugh and Win

http://www.hollywoodsquares.com/contestant
http://www.comedycentral.com/laugh/content.shtml
http://www.futility.com
Mix and mingle with celebrities and comedians, while you win cash and valuable prizes. Visit these sites to see how you can make the cut.

192
Web Riot

http://www.mtv.com/mtv/tubescan/webriot
Play alongside the contestants of MTV's game show. You can win cash and prizes like DVD players and guitars. There's also an online version where you can jump in and play against others over the Internet any time.

CHAPTER X
UNCOMMON KNOWLEDGE

193
Trivia Spot

http://www.triviaspot.com
It's no fun to know it all unless you can show it off to other people. Trivia Machine lets you compete against others in trivia contests for bragging rights and prizes.

194
American Pop

http://www.ampop.com/rec
American Movie Classics presents you with a different pop culture trivia question every day. Compete with others for the highest score.

195
Entertaining Trivia

http://www.eonline.com/Fun/Quiz
Test your Seinfeld IQ and show off your knowledge of child stars in this online quiz show from E! Entertainment.

196
<u>Stand Up and Be Counted</u>

http://www.uproar.com/games/blitz
Take the Family Feud survey, and let your answers count in the online game. Then, try the trivia quizzes for prizes in categories like movies and sports.

197
<u>The Simpsons</u>

http://www.snpp.com/guides/quizq.html
http://eonline.com/Fun/Quiz/Simpsons
http://www.cornboy.com/wonderquiz
How closely have you been paying attention? See how much you know about Homer, Marge, Lisa, Bart, Maggie and the rest of Springfield. These are must-see sites for any Simpsons fan.

198
<u>Pop Culture</u>

http://www.quizsite.com
Even if you spend all your time watching TV and reading comic books, you can show off your knowledge with these quizzes. You'll be challenged with tough trivia about Spiderman, Limp Bizkit, the WWF and Friends. See? You weren't wasting your time.

199
Trivia City
http://www.triviacity.com
No matter which category of trivia you seek, you'll find it here — travel, computers, science, art and more.

200
The Riddler
http://www.riddler.com
Challenge others over the Internet or play by yourself. The Riddler has a good mix of categories, such as literature, geography, entertainment, sports and history.

201
All About Trivia
http://gamecenter.about.com/trivia
http://trivia.about.com
About.com's guides bring you trivia links from throughout the Internet, plus weekly trivia quizzes on subjects from art to the Simpsons.

202
Didja Know?

http://www.didjaknow.com
This site lists five strange facts every day. Only one is true. Are you clever enough to distinguish fact from fiction? Give it your best shot.

203
It's About Time

http://www.time.com/time/time100/quiz/quizarchive.html
Time Magazine hosts a weekly quiz on the 100 most influential people of the last 100 years. You'll find all the previous weeks' quizzes in the archives.

204
It's Outta There!

http://www.baseball-links.com/trivia.shtml
For baseball fans, here's a trivia blitz about America's game.

"I HACKED INTO THE SCHOOL'S COMPUTER AND CHANGED ALL MY GRADES. THEN THE SCHOOL HACKED INTO MY COMPUTER AND DELETED ALL MY GAMES!"

205
Get in the Game
http://www.iis-sports.com/trivia
This site specializes in sports trivia, with over 5,000 questions about football, baseball, soccer and more. Play ball!

206
Stumped?
http://www.askjeeves.com
http://www.absolutetrivia.com
Stuck on a tough question? Don't feel stupid. Use these sites to find the answers and increase your TQ (Trivia Quotient).

207
Encyclopedic Memory
http://encarta.msn.com/features/challenge
This trivia challenge is linked to Microsoft's online encyclopedia, Encarta. Most of the questions are tough, and you have to answer within the allotted time. Whether you answer correctly or not, it links into the Encarta articles so you can read up for next time.

208
Family Trivia

http://www.funtrivia.com

At this portal, you'll find family trivia with over 45,000 questions. You can even create your own trivia game. If you're stumped, have the questions answered by one of the trivia fanatics on the message board.

209
World Trivia Champs

http://www.two-twister.com/cnof

Get the lowdown on the world's largest trivia contest, held every year. Do you have what it takes? You could be the next world champion.

210
It's a Trivia World

http://www.triviaworld.com

Get your daily dose of trivia with Trivia World's fact of the day. Try one of the quizzes from categories of movies, music, history, computers and geography.

211
Fun for Your Mind

http://www.mindfun.com/braingames

Before you get into the hot seat on Who Wants to be a Millionaire or Jeopardy, practice with these tough trivia challenges.

212
Brainstorm

http://www.brainstormer.com

This "pub style" trivia site has a few quizzes to test your knowledge.

213
Have a Few Laughs

http://www.amused.com/comedyblitz.html

Amused brings you a weekly trivia quiz all about comedy. Get them all right, and you may win a cash prize.

214
Quiz Yourself

http://trivia.gator.net
http://www.triviaone.com
http://www.uselessknowledge.com/quiz.shtml
http://www.puzz.com
http://www.triviacafe.com

These sites feature a variety of trivia quizzes—from easy to very difficult—in many different subjects.

215
Bible Brainiac

http://www.biblequizzes.com
http://www.bible-trivia.com

Test your knowledge of the Bible with these trivia quizzes.

216
Brain Blitz

http://www.brainblitz.com/trivia/generaltrivia

Here are links to trivia sites all over the Web.

217
This Day in Trivia

http://halife.com/daily/trivia.html

For example, what happened on this day in 1959? Find out at this site. You can also take a trivia quiz the old-fashioned way here. There are no bells and whistles and no computer scoring, but the answers sure are interesting.

218
Silver Screen

http://www.cool-movie-trivia.com

http://www.thecelebritycafe.com/other/quiz.html

These glitzy sites have quizzes on the latest flicks and Hollywood happenings.

219
For Golfers

http://www.cybergolf.com/trivia

http://www.golfquiz.com

They won't improve your swing, but these sites will test your knowledge of the game with golf trivia, puzzles and crosswords.

220
Quizland

http://www.quizland.com
http://www.cnynet.com/lite/trivia.htm
Did you waste a lot of time watching TV as a kid? Now's your chance to put that trivia to good use. Take pop culture quizzes and test your knowledge on subjects such as The Brady Bunch, Happy Days, 90210 and Elvis.

221
Knowledge Pays

http://www.dujour.com/mondotrivia
http://www.puzzledepot.com/trivia.shtml
Put your trivia knowledge to work. These challenges award prizes to the trivia elite.

222
Outer Space

http://www.pbs.org/deepspace/trivia
PBS presents trivia from The Mysteries of Deep Space. The quizzes cover the universe, alien life and black holes.

223
Webby World
http://www.main-net.com/mn/concourse/trivia/internet
How much do you know about the Internet? Find out at this site.

224
What's on the Net
http://whatsonthe.net/triviamks.htm
Here are links to over 1,500 trivia sites and trivia pages online.

225
Trivia Across the Web
http://www.inquizitive.com/quizportal.htm
Inquizitive offers you a quiz portal listing over 200 sites with trivia in the categories
of entertainment, general knowledge, sports and the world.

226
Trivial Pursuit
http://www.trivialpursuit.com
Play online, order copies of it (on CD-ROM or old-fashioned cardboard) and read the
history of this popular board game.

227
All About the 80s

http://www.80s.com/Trivia
http://briansworld.fcac.org/quizzes/quizzes.html

Test your memory of 80s music and movies. Saw Pretty in Pink a few times? Loved Duran Duran? You'll do great.

228
Presidential Knowledge

http://www.freep.com/news/inaug/trivia
http://www.americanpresidents.com/triviatid.html
http://www.quizsite.com/quiz/history/unitedst/presiden
http://pbs.bilkent.edu.tr/weta/citizens96/survival/shockwave.html

Remember who had wooden teeth? Who chopped down that cherry tree? See how much you know about U.S. presidents.

229
Tough Trivia

http://www.swishweb.com/Quiz

Here are some trivia quizzes in such categories as Human Beings, the Cosmos and the Olympics.

230
Science Fiction

http://www.phishy.net/trivia
This site has over 12,000 questions to test your knowledge of Star Wars, Star Trek and Babylon 5.

CHAPTER XI
JOCK CLICKS

231
In Jeopardy
http://www.station.sony.com/sportsjeopardy
Good with trivia? Play the sports version of Jeopardy and compete for cash.

232
NFL Red Zone
http://www.nflredzone.com
The NFL Red Zone covers all the video games from Madden to NCAExtreme, with news, reviews, cheat codes, demos to download and tips to help you compete.

233
Fantasy Football
http://games.sportingnews.com/nfl
http://football.cnnsi.com
http://footballchallenge.commissioner.com
Don't let the salary cap hold you back. Assemble an NFL dream team and compete for cash prizes up to $25,000.

234
Fox Sports

http://www.foxsports.com/fantasy
Fox Sports brings you fantasy baseball, golf and football leagues.

235
ESPN Games

http://games.espn.go.com
At this ESPN site, you can play sports-themed arcade games like Ultimate Bobsled, 2-Minute Drill and Soccer Shootout. You'll also find fantasy leagues plus a "3Play" which lets you form a team with athletes from different in-season sports.

236
Hoop It Up

http://baseball.fantasysports.yahoo.com/baseball
Manage your own team of real professional baseball players and compete against others' teams. Play a full season or jump in mid-stream.

"I installed a Flight Simulator on my laptop!"

237
More Fantasy Sports

http://www.smallworld.com
http://cnnsi.com/fantasy
Love statistics? Pick your game. These sites offer fantasy basketball, baseball, golf, football, hockey and motor sports games. They're free to play, and you can win cash.

238
Armchair Athlete

http://www.sports-gaming.com
The Sports Gaming Network has news, reviews, previews and cheats for sports games on Nintendo 64, PlayStation, Dreamcast and the PC.

239
Golf Fantasy

http://www.golfweek.com/fantasy
http://golf.fantasysports.yahoo.com/golf
Pick a team of professional golfers and take it through the World Golf Championship. Compete for up to $10,000.

240
Get Hooked

http://www.fbc2000.com

In the Fantasy Bass Challenge, you choose a team from professional anglers. You'll compete against others for prizes like bass boats.

241
Sports Arcade

http://www.alphasports.com

Play sports-themed arcade and statistics games such as Pick Master, Beat the Analyst and Wacky Ball.

242
Operation Sports

http://www.operationsports.com

Turn your PC into an arena. Operation Sports has reviews, demos and patches for PC sports games.

243
Racing for the Prize

http://www.nfrl.com

The National Fantasy Racing League has weekly leagues offering cash prizes. Pick your dream team and cross your fingers.

244
Figure It Out

http://www.e-jocks.com/webring/ring.htm

You can use the calculator to create customized fantasy football ratings. You'll also find a fantasy football Web ring, with links to leagues all over the Internet, and a cheat sheet to help you get the edge.

245
Ask the Pros

http://www.fflpros.com

Having a losing season? The Fantasy Football League Professionals can help. Ask the experts or discover the draft analysis.

246
Get Your Kicks
http://soccer.fantasysports.yahoo.com/mls
Yahoo's fantasy soccer league has weekly games.

247
Mac Sports
http://macsport.web.com
You'll find news and links to sports games for the Mac.

248
Sports Illustrated for Kids
http://sikids.com/games
Jump into some fun, fast-action games like OWNet Wrestling and Indy Frenzy.

249
Blitz Sports
http://www.blitzsports.com
Sierra's site links to sports leagues, utilities, and free sports downloads.

250
Don't Get Wet

http://www.footballpoolmanager.com
Football Pool Manager offers software to help you manage all your office and friendly sports pools. You can download a free evaluation copy at the site.

251
NASCAR Racing

http://www.fantasynascar.com
http://racing.fantasysports.yahoo.com/auto
Lead a team of real racing pros and compete against others throughout the NASCAR season.

CHAPTER XII
MIND MATTERS

252
Puzzle Me This

http://www.clevermedia.com/arcade
Put away those sharpened pencils; you won't need them for these cool Shockwave puzzle games. Try out your brain on games like Haunted Castle and Marble Jam.

253
Revenge of Rubik

http://byrden.com/puzzles
Remember Rubik's Cube? Here's your second chance to master it. This site has twisty puzzles of all shapes and sizes. The easy part is that you twist and turn the blocks with your mouse. The hard part is solving any of these puzzles. This unique site will have your head twisting and turning.

254
Alien Tiles

http://www.alientiles.com
Watch out; this one's really addictive. It's a rather simple, beautiful and completely mind-bending puzzle game.

255
Dilbert's Daily Challenge

http://www.unitedmedia.com/comics/dilbert/ddmw
Comic strip star Dilbert does his part to help you waste time at work. There's a special section with puzzles made just for your boss.

256
Jigsaw Puzzles

http://www.thepuzzlefactory.com
You don't need a lot of table space to put together these jigsaw puzzles. Just point and click. You can also send a jigsaw postcard to a friend.

257
Puzzle Maker
http://puzzlemaker.school.discovery.com
Do a teacher a favor by passing this site along; they'll love you for it. This cool and useful little site from the Discovery Channel helps you make your own puzzles for students, for newsletters or just to challenge a friend. You can create word searches, cryptograms and mazes.

258
What's My Line?
http://www.people.cornell.edu/pages/jad22
The puzzles at this unique site are simple. They give you the first line of a book, and you have to guess the book. It just might inspire a trip to the bookstore.

259
Puzzability
http://www.puzzability.com/puzzles
Play new puzzles every day. This site features Common Knowledge, a daily puzzle that plays like Hangman—with a twist.

260
A Puzzle a Day Keeps the Cobwebs Away
http://www.dailypuzzler.com
http://thinks.com/puzzles
These sites are where to go for your daily fix of crossword puzzles, word games, logic games, jumbles, word searches and trivia.

261
Quantum Puzzles
http://www.quantumbrainbenders.com
If calculus was just too easy for you, try the brain benders on this site. You'll be challenged with tough daily math puzzles. If you can solve these, Mensa should be your next stop.

262
Think Fast

http://www.tetris.com
http://hem.passagen.se/mnomn/tetrissida.html
The original, addictive game of falling blocks — Tetris — lives on the Web. Play online to your heart's content, and if you're the competitive type, you can compare your highest score with other players.

263
Bits and Pieces

http://www.bitsandpieces.com/arcade.asp
This arcade is from puzzle retailer Bits and Pieces. Play around with their many online jigsaw puzzles, word ladders and block sliders. New puzzles are added every two weeks.

264
Whodunnit?

http://www.mysterynet.com/thecase
Take a few minutes and try to solve one of these cute little picture mysteries. They're harder then they look, and there's a new, free mystery to try every day.

265
Play Cyber Detective

http://www.crimescene.com

Armchair detectives, take note. At this site, you'll read up on a very realistic case by viewing the evidence, exploring the crime scene and discussing the case with other players. You can play around at this site for free, but if you want to dig deeper into the cases, you'll need to sign up for a membership.

266
Create a Crossword

http://www.crosswordweaver.com
http://www.wordsearchmaker.com

If you've ever thought, "Hey, I could make one of these puzzles," now's your chance. Download a demo of some puzzle-making software and try your hand at the grid. Who knows? Maybe this could be your new career!

267
Exercise Your Brain

http://www.puzzles.cwc.net

Like variety? This site has crossword puzzles, trivia, word games and mind benders. There's something for everyone.

"My mom got me this game. Every time you blow up an alien, you have to stop and clean up the mess before you can continue to play."

268
Word Zap

http://www.wordzap.com
Download this action word game and play against others or against the computer.
Fans of Scrabble, Boggle and similar word games will enjoy this one.

269
Word Battles

http://www.funster.com
Give your mind a workout. Funster has word games you can play against others.

270
Freeze Phrase

http://www.freezephraze.com
It's like Wheel of Fortune without Vanna. The phrases you'll be figuring out are all from that neon and new wave decade—the 80s. Chat with the other players while you score points.

271
Crossword Helper

http://www.puzzledepot.com

If you need help with crossword puzzles or Scrabble, this site is a great resource. Use the Word Finder to come up with words that will fit in certain spaces.

272
Crossword Puzzles Galore

http://www.pimpernel.com/crosswords

http://www.bestcrosswords.com

What's the best thing about filling in a crossword puzzle online? You don't have to erase the wrong answers. Once you're finished, it looks like you didn't make any mistakes. Now, don't you feel smart?

273
Logic Your Way Out of This One

http://www.greylabyrinth.com/puzzles.htm

This site has some really tough logic games. There are no special effects; it's just you and your brain. The challenge? Be the first to post the answer. The prize? Serious bragging rights.

274
Brain Bashers

http://www.brainbashers.com

These will jump-start your mind. There are enough logic puzzles and games here to give your brain a real workout.

275
Tease Your Brain

http://www.brain-teaser.com
http://www.brainteasers.net
http://www.fitzweb.com/brainteasers

The entertaining and addictive little puzzles on these sites will keep you scratching your head for hours.

276
Puzzlers, Unite!

http://www.puzzlers.org

Hook up with other puzzle lovers worldwide, and try your hand at some samples. Word lovers will enjoy the list of 100 of the best anagrams of all time.

277
<u>Puzzle Experts</u>

http://www.dse.nl/puzzle
The puzzles at this site start out easy and then get really tough. Try your luck at math and logic brain teasers, or take a trivia quiz on a really obscure subject.

CHAPTER XIII
CHILD'S PLAY

278
Best of the Best

http://www.beritsbest.com
Berit's Best lists 1,000 of the best kids' sites on the Web. Look in the Just for Fun category for games, sports, coloring and activities.

279
Rainy Day Fun

http://www.funology.com
Funology has all sorts of fun things to do, both on and off the computer. Boredom Busters shows kids how to create something fun out of nothing. The Laboratory tells them about fun and safe science experiments. Kids will also find magic tricks, fun recipes and silly jokes.

280
Child's Play

http://www.bonus.com

This site provides games for kids — played in a protected browser window — so you can feel safe. There are plenty of creative and fun games to keep them occupied on rainy days.

281
So Weird

http://disney.go.com/DisneyChannel/zoogdisney/clubs/soweird

Disney's site is based on the popular children's show and features wacky arcade games and activities.

282
Cartoon Network

http://www.cartoonnetworkla.com

The Cartoon Network's official site is the home of games featuring the Powerpuff Girls, Tom and Jerry and Johnny Bravo.

283
Universal Kids
http://www.mca.com/home/playroom
Universal Studio's Kid's Playroom has games and activities based around characters from The Land Before Time, Casper and An American Tail.

284
Sports Illustrated for Kids
http://www.sikids.com/games
The popular kids' magazine has an online sports arcade with fun, sports-related video games and trivia.

285
Peanuts
http://www.unitedmedia.com/comics/peanuts
Visit Snoopy's dog house on the Internet. Charlie Brown, Linus, Lucy and all the Peanuts gang are here. Read the comic strip of the day, color the strips online or play Peanuts trivia.

286
Smart Kids

http://abc.go.com/tgif/games
ABC's Totally TGIF trivia for kids has, like, tons of questions. Ten are randomly selected for a totally tough quiz.

287
Family Fun

http://www.familygames.com
This site is chock full of family-safe shareware and freeware. You'll also find links to other family game sites, trivia quizzes and more family fun.

288
More for Kids

http://www.chevroncars.com
http://www.worldvillage.com/cat/games.html
These family-safe sites have a little bit of everything. You can play puzzles, word games, connect-the-dots and arcade games.

289
Kid Crossword
http://www.kidcrosswords.com
Here are plenty of colorful and fun crossword puzzles—just for kids—to print or play online.

290
Brain Teasers
http://www.eduplace.com/math/brain
Exercise your brain with a tough new teaser every Wednesday. Puzzles are sorted into grade ranges from 3rd through 8th, so you can match the right puzzle with your particular brain!

291
Sea Monkey Shenanigans
http://www.sea-monkey.com/shenanigans
Sea-Monkey Central has games and activities based on the silly TV show. Send a Sea-Mail Card to a friend, or play the Sea Monkey Scramble.

292
Tootsie Roll

http://www.tootsie.com/kids.html

Here's a fun site with trivia and games all about the chewy candy. Find out such Tootsie Roll secrets as why some wrappers have a picture of an Indian chief with a bow and arrow.

293
Turn Off the Computer

http://www.gameskidsplay.net

This site will get your kids away from the computer by showing how to play hundreds of real-life games. Find dozens of jump-rope rhymes, rules to such old favorites as Duck Duck Goose and Hopscotch, plus ball games, car games and more.

294
For Kids Only

http://www.squiglysplayhouse.com

http://worldkids.net/puzzles/puzzles.htm

This site has great rainy-day activities. Kids can play word games, solve some brain teasers and build their own stories.

295
Whiz Kids
http://www.familygames.com/features/quizzes.html
This site challenges kids on such subjects as Christmas, science and fairy tales.

296
It's Magic
http://www.funnybone.net/showroom
The Online Magic Showroom puts on a magic show just for you.

297
Lemonade Stand
http://www.littlejason.com/lemonade
This site brings a classic pastime to the Web. Kids set up their own virtual lemonade stand and see how successful they can make it. Young entrepreneurs will love it.

298
Kidworld
http://www.bconnex.net/~kidworld
Here's an online magazine for the younger set that is by kids, for kids. Participants can find online pen pals, read jokes, write stories and read stories by other kids.

299
Wacky Web Tales

http://www.eduplace.com/tales
Help write crazy stories by adding a few words, like the classic Madlib games. Kids can submit their own crazy stories, too.

300
Geography Games

http://www.eduplace.com/geo
Kids in grades four and up will enjoy this challenging game based on the geography of the United States. They must save the Earth from alien invasion by proving how much they know.

INDEX (BY SITE NUMBER)

Index (by site number)

INDEX (BY SITE NUMBER)

The Incredible Newsletter

If you are enjoying this book, you can also arrange to receive a steady stream of more "incredible Internet things," delivered directly to your e-mail address.

The Leebow Letter, Ken Leebow's weekly e-mail newsletter, provides new sites, updates on existing ones and information about other happenings on the Internet.

For more details about *The Leebow Letter* and how to subscribe, visit us at:

WWW.300INCREDIBLE.COM

(USO) United Service Organizations

For nearly 60 years, the United Service Organizations (USO) has "Delivered America" to service members stationed around the world, thousands of miles from family and friends. The USO provides celebrity entertainment, recreation, cultural orientation, language training, travel assistance, telephone and Internet access, and other vital services to military personnel and their families at 115 locations worldwide. The USO is a non-profit organization, not a government agency. It relies on the generosity of corporations and individuals to enable its programs and services to continue. For more information on contributing to the USO, please call 1-800-876-7469 or visit its Web site at www.uso.org.